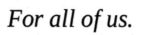

For all of us.

Two Hydrogen One Oxygen
A Children's Book about Water
A Story of Oceans, Baths,
and Swimming Pools

Text © 2021 by Tracey Johnson
Illustrations © 2021 by AllieAllDay

First paperback edition June 2021

I need the sea
because it teaches me.
Pablo Neruda

Children swim in the ocean
all over the world.
Sara loves the ocean
and so do her Mom and Dad.

Sara and her Mom
play in the swimming pool.
The water is cool
and makes them feel happy.
They float and splash and laugh,
feeling alive.

Mommy washes Sara's hair.
Only fresh water can wash
the soap off Sara's body
and shampoo off Sara's hair.
Only water can make a body clean.
Dad waits to dry the water off.

Even Sara's puppy loves water.
He feels it warm on his body.
Sara and her friend love washing
the puppy, especially
when he shakes the water off
and onto them.

Sometimes Sara feels sad and tears come. She knows her tears are okay. She knows her tears are made of water, water coming from her eyes. Her Mom hugs her for comfort.

Sara fills the birdbath with fresh water every day. All birds need to drink water to stay alive. They too want to stay clean, and water is the way of it.

Ice melts in the winter and becomes water of the waterfalls near Sara's house. Mom and Dad take her to the falls, to watch them, feel their power, and see their beauty.

All the vegetables that Sara loves best are found in her Mom's garden. For them to grow, they too need water. Sara waters the garden to make her garden grow.

Slurp, Sip, Coo

Sara and her Mom sip water

after their walk in the park.

Nothing quenches Sara's thirst

like water. It's delicious.

Sara sees rivers and lakes below and knows they are all connected at their source, the ocean.

Sara's Mom and Dad smile looking out of the window too.

We are all connected by water.
No matter where you are,
two hydrogen and one oxygen,
the elements of water,
bring us together.

Made in the USA
Las Vegas, NV
14 April 2023